Stickboy

5001

Also available from Shane. L. Koyczan
and House of Parlance Media, Inc.:

Visiting Hours

Stickboy

SHANE. L. KOYCZAN

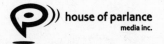
house of parlance
media inc.

House of Parlance Media, Inc.
202-1636 West 2nd Avenue
Vancouver, British Columbia, Canada   V6J 1H4
www.houseofparlance.com

Library and Archives Canada Cataloguing in Publication
Koyczan, Shane, 1976-

Stickboy : a novel in verse / Shane Koyczan.
ISBN 978-0-9738131-6-6
I. Title.
PS8621.O978S84 2008   C813'.6   C2008-903802-9

Editor: Tonya Martin
Front cover design: John Rummen
Back cover & interior design: Mauve Pagé
Printed in Canada by Webcom

10 9 8 7 6 5 4 3

For Them

"Survival isn't an instinct...
it's an act of sheer will...
get up."

—*My Grandmother*

I can only tell you how it felt...

Part 1

 **Preface.**

I can only tell you how it felt.

There wasn't much in the way of warning:
no air-raid sirens or red alerts.
Not even the wide-eyed, slow-motion expressions
   of shock and sympathy that
you might see on the face of someone watching
   a monster creep up behind you.
But I didn't see anything on the faces of those
   who saw it coming —
those who knew it was going to hurt.

If I had eyes in the back of my head —
or if I simply had a friend whom I could ask,
I might be able to tell you what it looked like.
But, as it stands, I can only tell you how it felt.

It felt like moving.

Suddenly.

Quickly.

And without warning.

Imagine that our nervous system is like
    the postal service.
Keep in mind that most of the things you want
    your body to do begin with a thought.
So, imagine you want to move your finger —
maybe it's uncomfortable in its current position,
or maybe you just want to show it to someone
    in that "fuck you" kind of way.
Regardless of the reason, there is a want,
there is a desire,
there is a thought.

So your brain writes a letter to your finger.
It licks the stamp,
seals the envelope,
then sends it on its way.

Soon enough it arrives at the nerve endings in your finger.
They read it.
There are the normal pleasantries accompanying
    most letters.
The standard, "How are things?

"Things here are good.
Could use some more caffeine, but, all in all, things
    are good."
The letter might go on to explain that there's an asshole
    standing in front of you,
and he deserves to know
what you, as a collective, think of him.

Next, there is the request —
it is never an order or command.
It is always asked with humility and etiquette.
"Could you please stand the finger up straight
so that we might have clear communication with this
    individual? Thank you."

The nerve endings in the finger comply,
and there you are
giving someone the finger.

Perhaps the someone is large and mean.
Perhaps he wears his muscles like a tuxedo,
and he looks good in them.
Perhaps his brain is writing ten letters
— eight to his fingers and two to his thumbs —
politely asking them to make fists.

Regardless.

My brain had not written any letters, and yet
I was moving.
Suddenly.
Quickly.
And without warning.

My brain wrote many letters in that instant.
No time for the normal good-natured remarks.
No time for chitchat or gossip.
The letters came across as rude.

Nonetheless, my arms complied,
and I remain continually amazed
at how willing we are to sacrifice our hands
in the attempt to save our face.

Regardless.

Most falls consist of our hands and arms springing
    into action,
like god jumping up from his sofa
when he hears about the pope
watching hardcore pornography on the Vatican satellite.

My arms and
my hands
were no different.

Now imagine that the ground was in love with the sky.
Imagine that I was a surgeon:
one who had just come out of the operating room
    trying to save the sky's life.
Like an impatient lover, the ground came rushing
    up to meet me.

If we consider that the ground is capable of love,
then we must assume that it also has the capacity
    for the opposite emotion.
It was as if I had just informed the ground
that the sky didn't have much time left.

I wasn't to blame.
I had no idea which circumstances had presented themselves
to cause the sky to end up on my operating table.
But I did everything I could to save it.
Does that mean anything to the ground?
Do my efforts make any difference?
Of course not.

The ground was hard.

The real pain always comes later.
Our Internal Postal Service also sends "packages"—
endorphins,
adrenaline,
and so on.

The true feeling from any experience like this
is something you might find in the sketchbook of M.C. Escher.
It always feels like a paradox.

To call it disorienting
is like saying Django Reinhart played the guitar
   with two fingers —
true, in principle.
But like a blind hitman on the verge of retirement,
he can't quite assassinate the intended mark.

The bewilderment of the situation is always mixed in with
   the senses,
and no matter how confusing it all feels,
your senses become sharp —
sharp enough to cut the corners on a circle.

One brief look up was all it took...

Part 2

1.

One brief look up was all it took.

I knew this boy from school.

His name was Chris.

He was two years older than me,
but was still in my grade.
Chris had been left behind,
like the skin of some reptile that had been shed.
A skin that took on its own life
and fell in love with revenge
to soothe the steady ache of abandonment.

He was knuckles wrapped in meat.
He drove his boot into my gut,
as if his toes were crash-test dummies
and my face was a computer measuring and recording
the damage.
An elbow came thundering down on my jaw
like prize-winning, turnip-sized hail.
And, like a birthday that sneaks up on you,
it came again.
And again.

The metallic taste in my mouth
was soon offset by a loud crunch inside my head.
Something slid down my throat with the ease
   of a body in a barrel
being sent over a waterfall.

My tongue went into detective mode,
inspecting the damage
and reporting back to me.
"It doesn't look good."

A sudden intake of air introduced me to a new pain;
it blazed from where there was once a full tooth.
Now it was something jagged
and my body seized up in a
"what the hell was that?!"
kind of way.

But the analysis of the new
and extremely unpleasant sensation
would have to be puzzled over later.

A fist plowed into my nose.
It felt the way my mother's foot must have
when her cheap leather boot
crashed into her boyfriend's bedroom door
after hearing an unfamiliar woman's moan
from behind the lock.
I was seven years old when that happened,
and I remember being astonished by her strength —
even when she turned to me
with tears in her eyes.
Holding my face in both her hands,
her words staggering out of her
like my drunken father from a bar,
"Don't you ever... don't you dare."

The flashback ended abruptly.
Blood pitched out of me
like pus from a zit
on the verge of exploding.
Against the winter backdrop,
it didn't look like anything other than blood in the snow.

It looked blatant.

A few more minutes
and I would be one of those names
that parents say to other parents
while hanging their heads low,
swinging them back and forth like pendulums of shock.

I would be a horror story
catalogued deep inside the Dewy Decimal system
of Chris' legend.
A flagged book that librarians would only lend
to the most-dedicated scholars of cruelty —
lent in secret
and studied by candlelight
on cold nights,
in dark rooms,
where the chill is enough
to straighten out the backs of crooked insects.

I was slightly more involved with my immediate
   predicament,
so I hadn't noticed
that it hadn't taken long for a crowd to gather.
But, finally, I saw them
standing around us both,
like the pillars of some makeshift coliseum
where children are thrown in for the amusement
   of others.

It was a testament,
not only to the complete fucked-up-ed-ness
of my youth,
but also to the jaw-droppingly useless townsfolk
with whom I existed.

That's all.
I didn't live.
I existed,
like a rock thrown into a lake and forgotten
somewhere under the surface.
I was there,
I existed,
but at that moment
even that very slight fact was in question.

They just stood there like scriveners,
ready to jot down the exact time
that my pupils would become fixed and dilated.
For a second I looked at them
as if my house was on fire.
Why weren't they carrying buckets of water?

Finally, an old man stepped out of the crowd.
He had a face like an over-steamed potato
   with a butter-knife jab for a mouth.
He said,
"You leave that boy alone."

He shook like a baby pine tree
in a tsunami.
But balled his fists
as if his fingers were like the tiny roots of that pine
gripping the earth's flesh,
and protesting against nature's plan
to rip it from her skin like a blackhead.

I saw him for what he was:
an old trunk in the attic.
But somewhere under time-worn photos,
under the failed marriages,
under patchwork quilts and keepsakes handed down
 to him
by his family —
somewhere under all of the history,
he had saved one last knockout punch,
and dug it out for this moment.

His courage was a lighthouse;
it illuminated the crowd's humiliation.
The light slowly circled away,
and the shame tattooed itself on their faces.
Forever.

My Inner Holy Man cradled my Inner Child
and gave one last blessing
for our withered gladiator:

"May you trespass happily into eternity and be welcomed
 upon your capture."

Then my Inner Holy Man turned his back on god
 with a finality so sharp
it must have given diamonds pause to second-guess
 their "forever" status.

My Inner "Former" Holy Man turned to face the crowd
and cursed them to remember that moment
for the rest of their excruciatingly long lives:

"May the sun shine constantly upon each dark corner where
 you seek to hide,"
he said.

The only pity he could manage
belonged to the unfortunate reaper
whose rotten luck it was to one day collect them.
Them being those who bore witness.

I didn't see him vanish —
I felt it.
The same way my mother must have felt
when every other pregnancy
evacuated her body
as if it were a building on fire.
I remember my Inner Holy Man being there
but can't recall anything about him.

If my heart were a
hand grenade
I would have ripped it
from my chest
and thrown it at them.
I wanted to scream as if my lungs
were made of paper
and I was holding a match
to them.

I wanted to haunt them.

I hadn't even noticed that the beating had stopped
until the old man spoke again,

"What did this boy do to you to deserve this?"

Chris didn't answer,
he just backed off like a wolf from his meal
after hearing a shotgun being fired into the air.
He gave me a "to be continued..." look,
then turned and walked away;
his heavy black boots crunching in the snow,
as if he were walking on old, dry bones.
The old man said,
"Come on then... I'll walk you home."
He kicked some snow over the blood I had spilled.
It was a shame.
I wanted people to see it.
I wanted them to come across it and wonder
    what had happened.
I wanted them to hope everything was alright.
I wanted them to pray.

I didn't have any of my own faith anymore.
I felt it might be helpful to borrow the faith of others.

"Does that boy go to your school?"

"Yeah."

"Did you do anything to make him mad like that?"

He was the first man who didn't accuse me
    of starting anything.
He genuinely wanted to know what had happened.
His voice was calm,
like someone who had finally come to terms
    with an awful tragedy.

"No."

"I see."

He continued.
"I was in a war once you know.
A big one.
Me and a whole bunch of other guys.
They flew us over the ocean,
and when we landed
they pointed us in a general direction
and said,
'Go that way until you hear people fighting.'
So we did.
It didn't take long,
and when we got there
they pointed us toward the fight
and said,
'Go that way until you're in the fight.'
So we did.
Sure enough we got into the thick of it,
and on it went for a very long while
with different people
telling us to go this way and that way.
And we did.

We didn't all come back though.
For the few of us who finally did,
sure enough,
there was someone else
telling us,
'Go that way until you get to the man at the podium, and he'll
   give you your medal.'
So we did just that.

And after,
there wasn't anyone around to tell us where to go,

so some of us headed to the bar and stayed there,
some of us went to the hospital and stayed there,
some of us went home and stayed there.
Some of us got jobs.
Others got married.
Some of us had kids
who grew up never really knowing
where we'd been and what we'd done.

You know what we did?"

"No."

"We stopped a man who was doing bad things to good people
    for no reason.
We all got hurt doing it.
Most of us got hurt in our hearts and our heads,
and I'll tell you a secret:
sometimes I wish I never went.
I think I'd have better memories if I never went —

but I can't change that now.

So just point me in the direction we need to go,
and that's where we'll go."

His small mouth split into a broken smile;
it didn't look forced,
it just looked like something he was trying
    to remember how to do.

Maybe it was different for him.
I was a mirror reflecting my own opposite.

Maybe his Inner Holy Man was still lingering,
and it was his Inner Child that had gotten into some
   stranger's car
and was gone.
No photos on the backs of milk cartons.
No search parties.
Not away.
Not out.

Just gone.

I pointed in the general direction of my house.

"Alright then,"
he said.

I began to walk.

It took a few minutes before I noticed
that he wasn't walking beside me.

He was marching.

2.

My grandmother opened the door.
The warmth inside the house sprung out into the cold
as if it had been locked up unjustly
and was waiting for the right moment to slip past
   the guards
and escape.
Maybe it would disguise itself immediately,
blend into the cold white,
and live in obscurity.

My grandmother's eyes locked on the bloody nose.

She put her hand to her mouth
like there was a crowd of people inside her and they were
all asking different questions at the same time.
But she had to silence them and deal with the situation
   in front of her.

"Excuse me ma'am..."

The old man interrupted.
I hadn't even gotten his name.

"Your son was involved in a bit of a scuffle
    with another boy..."

Bastard.

There was a chance I could have passed this off
    as an accident.
Now there were going to be all kinds of questions
    that I didn't have answers for.

"He's my grandson... thank you for bringing him home...
    please come in."

After we had taken off our coats and boots,
    she took me by the hand and led us into the kitchen.
As soon as her skin touched mine
I felt like a piece of overboiled asparagus;
my body went limp,
every muscle just relaxed,
each step was a struggle.

I think my grandmother half-carried me.

She put on a pot of coffee,
and invited the old man to sit down at the table.

"There are some cookies in the jar if you like.
You can help yourself.
I just want to take care of this little man first."

"By all means."

My grandmother turned on the kitchen faucet.
The water ran for a few seconds
before she began testing it with her hands.
After a few seconds more,
she carefully put my head under the faucet.

The water was warm,
and for a moment, I thought I was going to piss myself.
She slowly ran one hand through my hair,
and the other began to lightly rub my back.
Her hands went from making small to large circles
then back to small.

If compassion wasn't just a thing that people possessed from
    time to time.
If it was tangible —
if it could take shape — and
if people could go beyond just sensing it within themselves.

If they could feel it in a physical way,
it would feel like my grandmother's hands on their backs.

The water did a good job of camouflaging my tears,
but she could still tell I was crying.
My lungs lurched back and forth.
It felt like they were throwing themselves against
    my ribcage
like a mental patient who knows he's not insane,
but can't help raging against everyone
because no one will believe him.

She leaned into me,

"Shhh… it's over my sweet boy… shhh."

I could live countless lives and never know
    this love again,
which was fine by me,
as long as I could remember it.
As long as I could have it to pull out
on those hard days,
those impossible days

when the setting sun bleeds into the lakes;
the horizon pulled tightly across its belly
   like a samurai blade.

I made sure my Inner Scribe was recording this moment.
His hand moving swiftly to catch details,
as if they were drops of rain falling all around him.

My grandmother gently pulled me away from the sink,
dried my hair with a kitchen cloth,
then lightly began to wipe away the blood.
She smiled,

"You look like Rudolph the red-nosed reindeer."

It was a bad joke,
but it was enough to reassure me
that everything was okay now.

The old man chuckled to himself.

She put a cloth under the faucet and turned on
   the cold water.
"Okay then. I want you to put this cloth around your neck and
   take a seat. I'll get you some milk."

The cloth was damn cold, but felt amazing.
I hadn't even noticed how hot I was until I put it
   on my neck.
It was ridiculous.
It was freezing outside.
Why was I so hot?

My scientific conundrum soon took a back seat
to the large glass of milk in front of me.

Milk was a rare delicacy in our house.
It was usually reserved for cooking or cereal
  in the morning.
But to have a glass of it just for drinking?
Even my Inner Saint was tempted to go out
  and get hurt more often.

"So what happened?"

Goddamn.

I was so close to just enjoying my milk.
I didn't even know what had happened.
I mean, I knew I had gotten into a fight.
But I didn't know why.
Telling my grandmother that I didn't know why
  it happened
would only make her suspicious.
She'd be sure I was holding out on her.
And then the worst thing that could happen
  would happen:

She'd be disappointed in me.

Before I could answer,
my own Private Soldier came rushing to my aid
once more.

"There wasn't any reason for it.
The boy just jumped on him.
Your grandson didn't do anything."

Okay.

I could cross him off the Bastard List.

"I think that boy was just looking for trouble,
and your grandson looked wimpy enough to amuse him."

Bastard!!!

Wimpy!?!
Where did that word even come from?
Whimper?
Is that what I do?
No.
Dogs whimper.

Eight years from that moment,
I would learn that
eighteen-year-old guys begging for sex whimper.
And a few months after that eight years had passed,
I would learn that
eighteen-year-old guys who just found out
they're going to have a baby whimper.

I wasn't any of those things.
I went to Catholic school.
At ten years old,
I didn't even know what sex was.

He looked at me,
the concern written on his face like an important novel
that people always mean to read
but never seem to get around to.

"The things that you're going
to feel about what happened?
You don't keep them.
You let them out and send them
on their way."

The lines on his face narrowed into trenches.
It was impossible to tell how many regiments
    were hiding in there waiting to attack.
It was impossible to tell which ones belonged to time,
and which ones belonged to war.
There was no way of knowing where the scars stopped
and old age began.

Under the table,
my grandmother took my hand in hers.
She only ever squeezed my hand when something important
    was happening.
It was her very own Morse code.
She'd tap her fingers on my skin
until the vibrations traveled through the wires
    of my nerves,
and I could feel my spine tingle.

My Inner Code Breaker would be left feverishly translating
    the dots and dashes;
the messages were always the same:

"Pay attention now."

She wanted me to know things —
not just the things they taught at school.

She used to say,
"If it's something that can be taught,
it's something worth learning.
If it's something that can be explained,
it's worth understanding.
If learning and understanding are things you can do,
They're something worth trying."

I was ten years old.

Trying to learn experience.
Trying to understand wisdom.
Trying to try.

I tongued my jagged half-tooth
and tried.

3.

On the cold days
it was always the same.

I would watch my breath come out of me
and pretend I was superhuman and
capable of freezing anything with a single blast
   from my powerful lungs.

I would look around at the snow-capped trees and houses
and smile with a satisfaction so complete that
it was as if nature never existed,
and winter was my doing all along.

I must have wasted three birthdays
wishing it was true;
secretly hoping my powers would kick in
at the exact moment I blew out the candles.

Cake flying across the room,
crashing through the walls
like a vanilla cannonball.
My granddad looking at me,
his eyes
barely slits and

investigating me from behind a facial mask of icing.
Me staring back at him,
with the look of a dog that had pooped in his shoe
and gotten away with it.

It never happened though.
As hard as I wished for it,
I could never make people blow away like feathers,
and I don't ever recall wishing harder
than the day I saw Chris walking towards me.
It was only two weeks since our first encounter,
and I'd done a pretty good job of avoiding him
until that point.

But now he stormed toward me
with a "...and now for the conclusion" look in his eyes.

Panic gripped me like the "Oh Shit" handle
in a car swerving to avoid a deer on the road.
Dread paralyzed me like a deer hypnotized
by the headlights of an oncoming vehicle.

Inside me,
an accident was happening
in slow motion.

My Inner Bystander
was on the curb,
arms flailing as if in the throes of an ancient dance
performed to appease some vengeful volcano god.
I was a small village
about to be erased by a natural disaster
that (for whatever reason)
decided to take the shape of a twelve-year-old boy.

Chris cocked his arm way back;
not like the hammer of a gun,
more like the neck of a catapult.
It was primeval.
It was the first marriage of science and warfare.
It was hideous in its conception.
It was vicious in its intention.

His fist was a boulder.
It didn't sail.
It didn't glide.
It pushed and pulled its way through the air
like something never blessed with the justification
of ever knowing flight.

That fist barreled towards me
ready to crash through the tired stones
of a kingdom that was already
raising a white flag in surrender.

My arms went up.

Cheap, wooden-fence pickets;
not even capable of stopping a light kick,
let alone a Mack truck intent on tearing up
    the front lawn of my face.
Instinct kicked in like a song on a jukebox
    I'd never noticed before.
It would have been magnificent
if it hadn't been so useless.

The fist stopped midair
and dropped obediently
to his side;
a dog being called home
by its master.

Chris' shoulder pushed itself into mine,
with the intensity Van Gogh must have felt
when he thought painting his ear
was a good idea.

I fell out of Chris' way,
and he walked on,
as if he'd just stepped through a wall
and it was no big deal.

I must have sat there for five minutes,
sweat rolling down my face,
like the beads of an abacus
trying to calculate an answer for what had just happened.
Maybe, upon seeing my face,
he'd concluded that he had already made his point.

My right cheek had bubbled out,
making me look like a squirrel
only halfway finished collecting nuts for the winter.
The blue/grey/green welt under my eye
was a smear;
it looked as if someone had taken an old, overused eraser
and tried wiping away a wrong answer.

The school bell was a wet towel spun into a whip,
snapping at my bare ass and
effectively breaking me out of my trance.
I picked myself up as best as I could
and shuffled off to class
with all the enthusiasm of a vegan at a meat-and-dairy
    convention.

Upon seeing my locker,
it was obvious that
the thick, black letters stacked on top of one another
resembled a totem pole
telling me the story
of what kind of school year I was about to have.

It wasn't just letters strung together to form an insult,
it was a notice:
this was not a two-part mini series.
This was going to be episode after episode,
in an entire season,
of some unbearable melodrama,
of which Chris was going to make me
the star.

The janitor was already there,
trying to scrub the letters away.
Not an easy feat, considering they had been written
   in permanent marker.

Unsure what to do,
but needing my math textbook,
I said,

"Excuse me... I need to get my book."

"Alright,"

he replied, and moved aside.

My combination lock opened with ease,
and as I reached in to collect my book,
the janitor said,
"Maybe if you lost some weight,
things like this wouldn't happen."

My Inner Janitor threw my heart into a trashcan,
carried it out to the curb,
and watched my Inner Garbage Man dump it
   into the compactor,
hit the button, and drive off.

I never used a locker again.

4.

Being called to the principal's office in the middle of class
was a bit like having a meal prepared for you
    by Titus Andronicus:
it was never a good thing.

The secretary would always make the distinction
in her announcement.
If it was "... please report to the main office,"
it could have been something as benign as a message from
    your parents.
Or a forgotten lunch.

If, however, it was "… please report to the principal's office,"
it meant that your entire class
would let out a collective and drawn out *"wooooo…"*
All you could do was resign yourself to the fact
that no matter what your fate,
your class "mates"
would deem it worth mocking.

I remember once when it happened to another kid and
the class let out the "doomed" cry.
I suppose it's mostly meant in jest,
but he didn't return to class that day.

The next day our teacher told us
that his father had died in an accident.
I think we all felt bad,
but not one of us said we were sorry.
It was as if every time we saw him
shame would steal our voices.

You'd think
they would have learned something that day.
And yet, the ritual continued.

Who were these people?
What if my grandparents had died?
This was a Catholic school.
Where was their compassion?
What would their own parents say?
Why wasn't the teacher shushing them?
My stomach tightened.
And I felt it.

It wasn't the first time.
There was the small tapping in my gut
only this time,
it felt more like a kick.

Maybe it was only hunger,
but it somehow felt more urgent.
My Inner Doctor piped up,
"Maybe you're getting sick."

Only a few years earlier,
I remember talking with my grandmother
about where babies came from
and, as far as I could recall,
it wasn't common for boys...
but maybe I was pregnant.

I switched off my imagination.
At that point, the last thing I needed
was to start worrying about how
I was going to raise a child.

Whatever the feeling in my gut was,
it would have to wait.

For a moment, my thoughts evaporated.
It didn't take long for clouds to form
and rain down all of the horrible possibilities
that were about to present themselves.

For a second, the clouds broke.

Maybe my mom
had come back.
Maybe she was going
to take me by the hand,
lead me out the front door,
and we would just
keep walking away.

As if "away" was a destination.
A place we could one day reach.
And, upon getting there,
everything we left behind
wouldn't be a part of the past.

It simply wouldn't be.

A second later,
and I could hear thunder in the distance,
like the car of some mean drunk
pulling into the driveway late at night.

Maybe she was dead.
I didn't really know her,
but it was distressing
to think that she was dead.

I was ashamed at my lack of emotion
over the prospect of her passing,
and I would have asked god to forgive me
if we had still been on speaking terms.

I put the thought out of my mind
and opened the door to the main office.

My eyes measured the secretary:
if she looked at me, it was bad.
If she didn't look at me, it was worse.
If she couldn't stop looking at me, it was tragic.

I was ten years old and already a savant on office behavior.

She couldn't stop looking at me.

5.

Our principal was a tall man,
not outrageously tall,
just tall enough
that people would stop to ask his exact height.

He must have felt like he was in one of those
jelly-bean contests,
where people buy a ticket and write down a guess
of the exact amount of jelly beans contained in a jar.
The closest correct answer would win a prize.

Near as I could figure, the only available prize
would have been
some useless sense of satisfaction
that would have the winner
walking around all day
feeling like they'd accomplished something.
Friends patting him on the back
and thinking, *I wonder how he is with lottery numbers?*

The principal was on the phone when I entered
the office.
His arm shot out like a snake

that had been loaded into some kind of cannon.
It motioned to a seat in front of his desk,
and, as I sat, the snake reloaded itself;
only its head could be seen sticking out of the sleeve.

His conversation continued.
It was impossible to determine what he was engaged in,
just a lot of "hmmm's,"

    "uh-huh's,"

and the occasional "I see," which lightly peppered
whatever dialogue he was having.

Looking back on it now,
he could have been having phone sex.
A sweet, smoky voice on the other end seductively declaring,
"I'm wearing black lace panties..."
"Hmmm..."

A giggle and then,
"Would you like me to take them off?"

"Uh-huh."

A hint of false surprise in her voice
when she finally unveils her trump card
"Oh my god... I'm so wet!"

"I see," he said, only slightly disappointed
by her bringing up the good lord.

But at the age of ten,
I was more interested in the crucifix
that was hanging on the wall behind him
just above his head.

You could still see sharp flakes of plastic
jutting out of jesus' side
where the front and back of him finally met
and were assembled.

It was remarkably cheap,
as if god had looked into his wallet
then finally told the pope,
"You know that whole 'let there be light'
    and creation thing?
Well I'm pretty tapped after all that,
but here's the recipe for a little miracle I call... plastic!"

The principal shifted his eyes to me,
hung up the phone,
leaned forward,
and breathed heavily.

I could see the coffee in his mug ripple,
his nostrils hovering above it
like two exhaust pipes over a puddle of muddy water.

"Do you know who did that to your locker?"
Of course I did.
"No."

"This is a serious matter...
someone has defaced school property."

Oooooooh... is that what they did?
For a minute, I thought maybe they wrote
"FATASS" on my locker in permanent marker,
left it there for the entire school to see,
and got a good laugh at my expense.

Sarcasm has never really suited me,
but blood exited my brain.

It was like someone pulled a fire alarm.
The blood in my skull exited
and was quickly gathering in my fists.
Sarcasm was all I had to work with.

My mind reeled,
trying to straighten it all out.

Is he honestly trying to tell me that
he's more concerned with a few letters
written on a cheap metal locker?

I was ten,
not even considering med school.
And yet, I could still see that this
was the symptom of a much larger problem.

He asked me again,

"Are you sure you don't know who did this?"

Getting Chris into trouble would only make things worse.
It wasn't knowledge or wisdom or experience
that led me to that conclusion.
It was instinct.

I was an animal out in the wild.
A chunk of meat hanging in front of me like a blessing.
But I could tell something was wrong,
and no amount of hunger
could make me throw caution to the wind.

The principal leaned back in his chair and
the black leather squeaked
like a small man being dog-piled by a football team.

Suddenly the crucifix above his head
looked like an idea.
Like something he was thinking.
Something he would delight in getting away with
if parents didn't have a say.

"Well if you don't know who did it,
then you're going to have to take responsibility.
I'll have to give you detention."

I would have asked him if he was joking,
if I didn't already know that he so clearly wasn't.

Yes.
That's right.
It was me.
I just went around all day
calling myself "FATASS."

FATASS was my tag.
If I could somehow get over to Germany,
I would have taken up both sides of the Berlin wall
so they'd know that FATASS couldn't be contained
   by mere ideologies.

FATASS was everywhere.

I was even considering writing it in big bold letters
on the great wall of China,
so it could be seen from space:
FATASS was here!!!

It might have been cool
if hip-hop wasn't just
an underground movement at the time.
There was no concern over my well-being.

It was as if he had just hit a kid on the highway,
pulled over, and got out to see if his car was okay.

I wanted to reach across his desk,
grab his three hole punch,
and smack him across the face with it.
I wanted to watch his teeth fly out of his mouth
like confetti in some slow-motion parade
for which I was the only spectator.

I would have stood there
watching the parade,
with all the wonder and amazement
of a child who still believes in Santa Claus.
Or
(at the very least)
like an adult
who still believes that stuffed-crust pizza
was a truly inspired idea.

The principal gave me another opportunity to fess up.

All I could think of was Chris.
Of how much worse
it could all be.
Detention was something
I could deal with.
Death was a much
deeper issue.

It was fairly obvious *he* knew
that *I* knew something.

How could he not?

He didn't have to be a Dark Knight Detective
to figure it out.
The bruises were a telltale story,
written on my face in blue-and-black ink.

"Do you want to tell me who gave you those bruises?"

Why?

So you could pretend to be a child again,
and play connect the dots one last time?
Silence was a puddle of cold piss
and I just sat there.

Sitting in it.

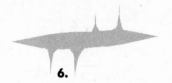

6.

"Detention" is what the world would be doing
every Sunday morning,
if confession had never been invented.

People would punish themselves over
their own guilty feelings,
then head out the door
on a mission to accrue more guilt.

A ten year old would have little to
compare it to.
But if my present-day self
might interject for a moment,
I'd say it's a little like picking an ingrown toenail,
at the end of a long day.
It's painful
but, like questionable sex,
we do it anyway.

Detention wouldn't have been so bad,
if Chris didn't happen to have it as well.
If he didn't choose to sit right behind me
in a room full of empty desks.
If he didn't keep kicking the underside of my chair.

I wanted to just turn around
and ask him, "Why?"

Why to all of it:
the fight;
the locker;
the kicking at my chair?

Why?

I'm not sure how it came about,
but I began thinking of Adam and Eve,
of how they existed in a paradise
perfectly tailored to their every need:

clouds of meat
slowly roasting to faultlessness
by the flame of an eternally warm sun.
Cheese slowly dripping over waterfalls —
but immaculate.
Not like that yellow sludge
that we everyday people smother our convenience-store
   nachos with.

It was lovely.
Every tedium entertained.
Every hurt mended.

But they didn't know anything.

It must be where the saying,
"Ignorance is bliss" comes from.
They just lived in their divine little garden,
content not knowing anything.

In order to learn —
to discover —
they would have to eat from the Tree of Knowledge.
So they did.
And they were cast out of paradise,
straight into chaos.

When they arrived here,
all they really knew for sure
was that it sucked.

I hadn't eaten any forbidden fruit.

I didn't know anything.
But I was pretty sure that this, too, sucked.

My revelation was interrupted by Chris
continuing his assault on my rump.
At that point I was convinced
that getting the answer to my question
couldn't be any worse then this.

Finally, I asked him,

"Why are you doing this to me?"

His eyebrows shot up in surprise,
then slowly deflated to a slightly lower position
    on his face.

"Because."

And there it was:
chaos.

"Because."
The one-word answer that people used for everything.
It meant absolutely nothing.
When finally pressed for an explanation,
the reprehensible truth just slithered away.

He had no reason.
He was the dirty joke
that your father tells you when facing puberty —
much like the dirty joke my dad told me
a few years later,
before he became a magician
and learned how to vanish.

"Son?"

"Yeah, Dad."

"Why do dogs lick their balls?"

"Gee, I don't know, Pops.
 Why do they lick their balls?"

"Because they can, Son.
 Because they can."

I turned back around
and faced the blackboard.
Without moving from my seat
(and not knowing it at the time)
I had taken my first step
into a steaming pile of crap
otherwise known as chaos.

7.

Weeks were like people:
eventually they passed.
And a few of them had done so
without incident.

I thought that maybe
asking Chris why he was doing this to me
had given him pause to really stop and reflect on it.

Perhaps he had come to a sort of beautiful conclusion,
the way my mother did
when she finally resolved
to leave an abusive relationship.

Or maybe he was just stalled at a crossroads,
kicking stones, and asking a guitar player for advice.

Whatever it was,
I was in no position to test my good fortune.
Even the fattest boy
or the heaviest man
could,
when the occasion called for it,
walk lightly upon eggshells.

Could
tiptoe over heavy coins of gold,
careful not to disturb whatever horrible dragon
was guarding them.

Sometimes we are so mindful of danger,
so concentrated on the awful possibilities,
that we can almost make ourselves invisible.
We become illusionists;
learning to walk in the periphery
of those who would look for us.

We are always only slightly there.

But we become so vigilant
in our quest to avoid drawing attention to ourselves,
that our absence itself becomes a type of attention.
Our silence becomes a kind of credential
that we wear like a nametag.
At first, people don't even realize
they're hearing it.

But the more we are absent,
the more we are amplified.
Until, inevitably, the low hum
of our invisible force field
finally reveals us.

It didn't take long
for the entire school
to turn their heads in an attempt to discern
where that sound was coming from.

Of course,
once they did,
all that remained
was for them
to shut it down.

And,
at that point,
I might as well have thrown
a book of matches at god
and asked him to set the world on fire.

Might as well have thrown a shovel
at my principal and said,
"No headstones.
No markings
... and make it deep."

Spit . . .

Part 3

8.

Spit
is something you do
when there is a bad taste in your mouth.

Or
when you have sucked the snake
venom out of your friend's leg.

Or
when you finally remove that stubborn piece of meat
that had been stuck in your teeth,
and was slowly driving you mad.

Spit
is even acceptable
after clearing your sinuses.

Or
like my mother,
upon discovering that her faithful husband
had come up short on faith,
and was full of something else entirely.
Namely, bullshit.

I was thirteen now.
Three years past my first beating.
Two years past Chris and his family moving away.
One year into a new cast of characters
devoted to making me the focus of their idle time.

The inventor of the iron maiden,
the crow's nest,
the rack,
the heretic's fork,
the Catherine wheel,
the Judas chair,
the crocodile shears,
and the lead sprinkler,
would all have cause to kneel in respect
to the twisted mind
who came up with the idea of
dangling spit over the face
of a subdued and intended victim,
then sucking it back up at the last minute.
My Inner Mathematician threw up his hands
and shouted:
"These equations are impossible.
I can't calculate any of it.
It makes no sense!"

It happened the same way it always did.
Three boys had pinned me down;
one on my chest,
one at each shoulder and arm.
I remembered my granddad saying,
"Bad things happen in threes."
And, while it was three boys who were doing this to me,
it was the umpteenth time it had happened.
And it showed no signs of getting any better
than the first three times it had occurred.

Jeff,
the boy on my chest,
had a mouth like Mick Jagger
and eyebrows that were always cocked in fascination —
like Mr. Spock.

His two toadies,
— Halian and Curtis —
laughed the way cavemen must have
when they invented whatever grunt it was that meant
"dickhead."

I could feel tentacles reaching up
from inside me.
There was some THING
living in my bile
and, like a man buried alive by mistake,
it desperately wanted out.

Whatever it was,
this thing wanted to tear open my stomach
and let the acid melt its way through my belly,
so it could pour out into the world
and satisfy a hunger so drastic,
that once it consumed the world
it could
(and would)
eat itself for dessert.

I could feel it jolting
around inside me,
struggling to break free from
the tangled mess of my guts.
And, for a brief moment,
I thought I heard it scream —
as if its own sheer will
had somehow given it a voice.

It was the same moment
that a fact was made clear:
A fact that I had no aptitude for science.

More specifically, physics.
More specific than that:
the aerodynamics and effect of gravity on spit
when trying to achieve a vertical launch from
the ground control of my mouth
to the upper atmosphere of Jeff's face.

I spat *up*
into Jeff's face.

I watched the spit strain upwards
like a swimmer on his last whisper of breath,
just inches from the surface of the ocean.
His fingertips barely breaking the crust of life
and touching, once more,
what so clearly outshines
the magnificence of any great fortune.

It is no secret
that those who have cast god
out of the garden of their hearts
will —
when desperation breathes the word "quit"
into their ears; when the mere consideration
of surrender feels like the steady gush of that first orgasm.

Will —
when the temptation to submit
sheds on us a glimpse of peace,
then declares it the reward to be granted
in the moment we acquiesce.

Will,
will,
will.
It is no secret that we
will
call on god once more.

Unfortunately for me,
prayer was a cell phone
that, no matter what peak I climbed to,
would not receive a signal.

My spit
was a foolish child
giving up the trading Card of Momentum
for the lesser-valued Card of Gravity.

If I could see it again in slow motion,
it would probably have looked like an old man
walking to the store,
then turning around halfway —
realizing he'd forgotten his wallet.

My own spit
betrayed me,
like a son ousting his own father
from the company his dad
had built into an empire.

It would have been Shakespearean,
if it wasn't so pathetic.

My own spit
landed in the corner of my right eye,
and the three boys toppled over like low-rent housing
being demolished to make way for another mall
that no one needed.

I imagine that a little piss dribbled into their tighty whiteys
as they clutched their sides,
feeling the tremendous paradox
of a laughing fit.

Joy was the peanut butter
and agony was the stale bannock
on which it was spread.

Still they feasted.

9.

New and old bullies came in and out of my life
as effortlessly
as breath.

"FATASS"
had become so much more than a word scrawled on a locker.

It was a permission slip.

It was a sign stating "Open Season."

One by one,
they found me in their crosshairs,

and squeezed their triggers in the same way
they must have gripped their fathers' fingers
after being born.

Bullets fly too fast;
any pleasure to be siphoned off my misery
would have to come from the slow squeeze of the trigger.
Anticipation
was,
and will always be,
the sold-out stadium that cheers our imaginations on.
The anticipation of any first time.
The anticipation of losing our virginity.
The anticipation of the first high after the first hit
of a drug we've never tried.

What will it be like?
We wonder.

And rarely is our imagination outdone.

Our minds paint masterpieces
that leave the Picassos and the Rembrandts
grumpily nursing warm beers,
as they bemoan their creative impotence.

But never will we get those first times back.

Even a tree that regrows its leaves in the spring
is utterly aware that not one of those leaves
will measure up to the first leaf it grew.

That one leaf, which eventually yellowed,
curled up,
and floated away
as the wind blew goodbye-kisses to the summer.

That one leaf was greener.

That one leaf
gave the still-growing tree pause
to marvel at its own ability.

And that tree,
which could very well live for another 400 years or more,
knows full well the permanence of what has happened.

Every fall,
we gasp at the brilliant colors
that Death mixes on his palette.
Somehow we fail to take note of the trees themselves,
and how the ferryman wind
affectionately shakes their branches
so that the trees themselves may wave farewell
    to their leaves.

I hated the fall.

Because everything else
I hated came along with it:

the cold weather;
the beginning of school;
the heavy clothes.

The bullies.

When I was young, fall never felt like an ending.
It was always the start of something
and, as one year bled into the next,
so did I —
over and over again.

Like a wound that never heals.

I remember the old man telling me,
"The things that you're going to feel about what happened?
You don't keep them.
You let them out and send them on their way."

But how could I?

One short summer
of being dunked in the lake until I almost drowned,
the gum in the hair,
the stolen money,
the stolen bike,
the beatings,
the extortion.

And then came September,
when they waltzed back into my life.

Their dance cards filled with my name.

10.

Getting a bully into trouble
was like taking communion without understanding
that the piece of bread they give you
is a metaphor,
and not actually a piece of the body of christ.

It was worrisome.

But even without intention,
it would happen.

Sometimes a teacher would catch them in the act,
and send both the victim and victimizer
to the office.

The principal always had the full story from the teacher,
but would, nonetheless, want the reason for it.
That's when the standard threat came into play:
"Say anything, and you're dead."

Since he was already going to get into trouble,
it might have been more accurate for him to just say:
"You're dead."

Which,
after being punched and kicked repeatedly,

I was sure
he was already trying to achieve.

My Inner Philosopher just sat there like a felled tree.
Stumped.

The one time I experimented with
telling the truth,
the principal called me "a rat."

Citing that I was without honor,
and that it should be quite obvious
why I didn't have any friends.

That it should be quite obvious
why I was being picked on or made fun of.

In retrospect,
it was quite obvious
that my principal
should have been fired.

He was disappointed in me
when I didn't respond.
He was disgusted with me
when I did.

Two equally useless paths
set out before me
like a prison meal and starvation.
An inmate only eats
because life, it seems,
cannot get any worse.

There was no less-traveled route
that would make all the difference.

There was no difference.

I might as well have been sitting
in a room
with no doors
trying to invent my way out.

I was too embarrassed
to tell my grandparents,
too scared to tell my teachers.

My Inner Community
became my Inner Mob —
storming the castle,
and demanding a new government.

Everything that follows
is the result of my surrender.

My granddad brought it home one day...

Part 4

11.

My granddad brought it home one day,
and, at first,
it was a lot like a championship bridge game.

It had all the tension,
all the heart-racing excitement,
all the thrills and drama.

And I couldn't have cared less.

Until my granddad asked,
"Would you like to hold it?"

I took it in my hands and was immediately impressed
by its weight.
It just felt like everything I was lacking.

It felt strong.

It was a .22 rifle
with a scope for aiming precision,
and an eleven-bullet clip.

I wasn't sure —
nor did I care —
what kind of wood
or
what kind of steel
it was made of.

It looked like that perfect couple.
Those two people
that the neighbors are always jealous of.

The best part
was the loading bolt.

The way it slid back and forth,
perfectly.
Like something I would learn about a few years later.

There was the saccharine *click*
when the mechanics finally locked together,
like the embrace of a true love
after returning from a long absence.

Or,
at the very least,
like a dog waiting at the door
for you to arrive home.

We drove out to the shooting range
that same day.
Me,
my uncle,
and my granddad.
All of us, barely breathing.
Our lungs crushed by the impossible weight
of anticipation.

It was a forty-five minute drive to the range,
and granddad was a dedicated fan
of Austrian and German drinking songs,
which meant we were forced to listen
to music we couldn't understand.

My memory trickled back to a Sunday drive,
years ago,
when my grandmother
made the mistake of asking,
"What is this song about?"

"Listen to the chorus…,"
he smiled,
"It's about a girl named Veronika."

You could almost hear the "k" in Veronika
as the happy drunks belted out her name.

You could almost feel her daydreaming that her name
    was spelled with a "c,"
as if changing that one letter meant more
    than a different lineage —
it meant a different life.

"Well I can *hear* that it's about a girl… but what
    about her?"
my grandmother pressed.

My granddad threw his head back in laughter,
"It's about a whore my darling… it's about a very
    experienced whore."

After that particular Sunday drive,
I immediately looked up the word "whore"
    in the dictionary,
but found myself having to also look up the words
"promiscuous,"
"intercourse,"
"prostitute,"
"harlot,"
and "strumpet."
All of which led me further from understanding *anything*
    about Veronika.

Toward the end of my research, I was convinced
that a whore was
a man of no fixed occupation, who was
indiscriminate when it came to mingling,

and used his talents in a shameful manner
  (and usually for money).

Also "he" was (for some reason)
a bad harpsichord player,
and capable of interchanging thoughts
with others like him.

You can imagine my surprise
the day my music teacher told us he was leaving
to pursue a different path.

Looking back,
I probably should have waited until the end of class
to ask if he was planning to become a whore.

My principal was also ineffective in explaining to me
what a whore was,
only stating that I should avoid them, if possible.
His answer only confirmed my suspicions
that somewhere — far away —
there were other young boys
who were already far more prepared for life than me.

My brief flirtation with nostalgia ended,
when, finally,
we arrived at the shooting range —
all of us snubbing the cold
like a fifteen-minute celebrity
asking us for the time.
At first,
they would only let me set up the empty pop cans,
but my patience (and refusal to whine)
won them over.
And even though they had only made several hits,
they insisted on giving me advice.

I took their careful instructions,
and missed the first two times.

My granddad —
ever the penny pincher —
spoke up,

"You're wasting bullets."

I felt the tiny kick of each shot;
it reminded me of something.

The third shot was clarity:
everything lined up
like grocers at the checkout on coupon day,
minus the irritation.

I could see the orange pop can,
the crosshairs of the scope
running through it,
dissecting it into four equal parts,
and meeting in the middle like nations
so exhausted by war
that their beds became an idea
more attractive than victory.

The trigger practically told me how to touch it;
one light and steady squeeze.

The can leaped into the air,
like a shuttle blasting off
on a mission to put the green-cheese myth to rest.

There are giants,
kings,
even moguls

who could not know
the intensity I felt inside.

At its closest,
the sun is roughly 146 kilometers from the earth.
Its light takes approximately eight minutes
and eighteen seconds
to reach us.

It was as if I had cut that time in half —
but only for me.
It was as if the sun would shine for four minutes
and nine seconds.
Just for me.

I felt like all I had to do was think it,
and the sky would bend for me;
its back arched like the inner thigh of a hula-hoop.

I put down the rifle,
walked behind the car,
unzipped my pants,
and baptized the earth with my piss.

The rifle lived in my grandparents' bedroom closet
or rather,
it waited to come alive.

On the rare occasions
when I was left home alone,
I would take it out,
careful to note
the position of everything
so no one would know I had been in there.

Just like Christmas,
when I would meticulously keep an inventory
of what gifts there were,
and which ones would go
to which person.

It was a guessing game
that I had gotten pretty good at
and, even though I always felt guilty doing it,
it was like checking under your uncle's mattress
to inspect his late-night reading habits.

I knew it was wrong.
But I did it anyways.

It was different with the rifle.

My other misdeeds were done out of curiosity;
I wanted to know something.

With the rifle,
I just wanted to hold it —
to feel its weight.

As if confidence,
respect,
power,
were all things that could be measured on scales.
And if I could add these missing ingredients to myself
I could somehow be made equal.

I thought about my school,
how the hallways would fall silent
like heaven might,
if god stubbed his toe
and took his own name in vain.

Gabriel ushering god to the gates
saying, "Sorry... but rules are rules."

I thought about Chris.
I was sorry he wasn't at my school anymore.
I imagined him
fumbling for an apology,
his tongue tripping over the words
like a newborn deer
trying to negotiate its way down a rocky hill.

12.

I thought about Jeff and his two minions.
I thought about how their loyalty would disintegrate
before his eyes,
like a popsicle held up to a mechanic's blowtorch.
All his confidence would just melt away
and collect into a thick pool at his feet.

I thought about the three girls
who thought it would be funny
to dare the boys with crushes on them
to mutilate the spokes on my bike tires.

The three girls who
thought it would be a prank of such hilarity
to have someone set fire to my clothes during gym class,
or "accidentally" spill boiling water down my back in home
    economics —
just to watch me shriek as the teacher pulled off my shirt,
and tissue-paper sheets of skin just fell off
like poorly applied strips of paper mache.

I thought about how it would look
to see their shields of beauty and charm
finally abandon them.

I thought about the saying,
"beauty is only in the eye
of the beholder."
And then I imagined The Beholder
gouging out his own eye,
just so he wouldn't have
to care about them anymore.

But mostly,

I thought about those

who said or did nothing.

The mute witnesses
who had sewn their eyes shut,
and refused to eat from the tree of knowledge.
Refused to know anything
about what was happening —
as long as it wasn't happening to them.

I imagined my superhuman breath
kicking in, at last.
It was so astonishingly forceful
that it uprooted their paradise
and blew it past myth and legend.
So that even existence would claim amnesia
upon trying to remember it.

I imagined them standing there,
where bliss once lived.
Their feet no longer carpeted by the warm grass of ignorance.
I imagined that I had hurled them into knowing,
and their eyes widened with shock
knowing it was all about to become
very not good.

I felt a callus growing around my heart.
As if my new government
was building a fortress inside me
and, somewhere behind those walls,
everything about me was being retrained,
militarized.
My Inner Community —
once vibrant with opinion and wonder —
had now been sharpened into simple points,
reduced to "yes" and "no-sir" answers.

Finally,
patience recognized my commitment,
and I was rewarded with two paths —
set out before me
like red carpets.
Each one leading to very different
movie premieres of my life.

The heavy hands of choice landed on my shoulders;
each one massaging the conflicting aspects of my
   consciousness
into a decision.

It came down to one question:

could I allow myself to absorb any more of this life
with no consequence to those who had misshapen it?

No sir.

I could not.

It was a Monday...

Part 5

13.

It was a Monday.
I remember, because my grandmother
would always have to leave early for work,
and I would have to see myself off to school.

She wasn't even one minute out the door,
when I shot up the stairs
like a bullet on its way to a date
with a president.

Like so many times before,
I was careful not to disturb
the placement of anything in the closet.
It hardly mattered at that point,
but it had become a ritual of sorts.

Almost like a smoker who rolls his own cigarettes.
He might have just been informed about the tumor
    in his lungs,
but the addiction fools him into thinking that
he needs one more in order to deal with the stressful
    situation
(even though it was that same mentality
that kept him lighting one after the other

until the ashy hands of cancer
finally took hold of his lungs
and began popping the alveoli
like the plastic packing bubbles
that people use to send gifts
that are not nearly as fragile
as those they send them to).

There's no real enjoyment in the cigarette itself;
it's the ritual.
The slow anticipation,
the foreplay of addiction.
Until addiction itself becomes a kind of geisha,
knowing exactly where,
when,
and how to touch you.

Power, too,
is a kind of drug.
Different because it remains ethereal;
more of an idea,
than a substance.
There was no danger of turning my veins
into a sewer system.
But the more I thought about school,
the more I was gripped
by that once-small thing
that lived inside me.

I removed the clip from the rifle,
and, one by one, loaded the eleven rounds.
The light feel of metal grinding on metal —
of placing one bullet on top of the other —
was in its own way a trigger,
as that first rush of expectation
blasted images into me.

I imagined the first round,
advancing in the chamber
like the last footsteps
of an innocent man
on the heavy walk
to an electric chair.

I could almost feel the bolt
sliding back, then forward,
and locking into place
as the next round went up to bat.

I thought of "Casey At The Bat."
I thought of how ego whispered itself into Casey's ear,
and, like a parasite, destroyed his humility —
leading him to believe he was invincible.

And then,
at the moment when he should have connected
with the baseball,
when the loud *crack* of contact
between the ball and the bat should have rung out
as if Casey himself had broken the world's arm.

At that precise moment,
when the fans should have exploded into celebration —

nothing.

All of his poise was
ripped away like a bandage
revealing the wound
of his over-confidence.

I wouldn't let two perfectly good pitches go by unchecked.

I would swing at them all.

I put the clip in my pocket,
and felt the light *clink*
as it made an acquaintance out of my house key.
(I'm not sure what those two would have to talk about
on the long walk to school.
Maybe nothing.
Maybe just awkward conversation,
both of them reciting weather forecasts,
    sports scores, and
digging deep holes in the earth
searching for the buried treasure of a common ground.)

I slid the remaining box of bullets into my knapsack.
I could hear them
rattling against the plastic tray that held them in place.
They sounded like prisoners
dragging their cups along the bars of their cells
because something was about to happen.

The rifle was,
at first,
a conundrum.
I couldn't just sling it over my shoulder
and head out the door.

I imagined cars sliding into telephone poles
as the drivers hit their brakes,
trying to decipher the intentions
of a boy, in the early morning,
marching down the sidewalk
with a rifle strapped to his back.

I pulled my snow pants out of the closet.
I hated wearing them,
but they were, on the extremely cold days,

a necessary evil.
Kind of like having to take a shit
in a crowded public restroom;
it's quite obvious what we're up to in that bathroom stall,
but we really don't want anyone to hear our efforts.

I began to slide the rifle down the right leg
   of my snow pants.
I would have to tuck the barrel into my boot so it wouldn't
   stick out.
but the stock would be perfectly concealed
   by my winter jacket.

I wasn't fond of the idea
of having to walk all the way to school
straight-legged,
like a robot whose right knee was malfunctioning.
But determination lent itself to me
and, because it asked for nothing in return,
I had no problem borrowing it.
I sat on the floor of the foyer leading to the front door,
inching the snow pants up around me.
The few snags and catches
didn't even frustrate me.

I don't recall that I
second-guessed myself.
Until my grandmother
swung the front door open.

She didn't say anything.
Didn't raise her voice to heights
that mountains take pause to admire.
She didn't yell or scream.

Her eyes didn't narrow with outrage,
or widen in disbelief.

Her jaw didn't drop like a carnival ride
built for the sole purpose of thrilling the bored.

She didn't fall to the floor
as if it were the top of an altar
where she lay her body in sacrifice —
hoping that it would stop something awful from happening.

She simply closed the door behind her,
sat down next to me,
unbuttoned her winter jacket,
and sighed one heavily labored breath —
as if this moment were a long pregnancy,
whose tremors of pain had finally begun,
and she had recognized the fact
that this was when the real work was about to start.

"I forgot a recipe for work,"
she said.

Her hand slid slowly up my back
and lightly pulled the toque off of my head.
Her fingertips moved in small and large circles around my
    scalp;
she knew that toque always made my head itchy.

"I love you.

I love you so much

my sweet boy."

Every hair on my body stood up like a white flag
   in surrender,
and I buried my face in her shoulder,
hoping that it would never be exhumed.
And I could just rest there,
until time turned its attention to the future once more,
and forgot all about me.

"I love you.
I love you until the stars burn out.
Maybe I didn't say as much as I should have,
but I promise I love you."

The release
was so total.
Secrets poured out of me like lemonade
at a stand open for business
in the middle of a desert;
where millionaires threw thick rolls of cash at me
   for just one drink,
because the cost of living was outrageous
and bare-bones survival was all they could afford.

We sat there
for the large part
of a long while.
We sat there
and talked.

We talked until the phone rang,
and her boss asked her why she wasn't at work.
Then she sat back down,
and we talked some more.
We talked until the phone rang again,
and the school asked her why I wasn't there.
Then she sat back down,
and we talked some more.

She told me that fantasies are appealing
because we can't see past them.
That when we are in the midst of a fantasy,
we are like horses with blinders on
that narrow our vision,
and never allow us to see the true scope
of what our actions entail.

She told me
it wouldn't just be them to suffer,
it would be their families —
and worse —
it would be my own family.

She told me that they would take me away.
She told me how much that would hurt her.

She said,
"One day this will all pass
and because of it,
you will be strong in a way others are not.
But you must learn to navigate your own life;
your choices
will affect others,
so think them through.
I know you can't possibly want to hurt everyone.
Please don't hurt me."

We stayed home the rest of the day,
and promised not to say anything about it.

When my granddad came home from work,
he didn't ask why my grandmother was home from work
    early.
He was just happy to see dinner waiting on the table for him.

We carried on
as if it was just another day.
there were only slight differences:

an early dinner,
served with a glass of milk.

The rifle did not suddenly leave our home.
It wasn't made prisoner behind lock and key.

I simply never touched it again.

Endurance is a funny thing...

Part 6

14.

Endurance is a funny thing.
There are times
when we feel like a car on empty,
sputtering to a stop,
only five miles away from gas.

Other times
are exactly the same,
the only difference
is that we make it
to that gas station.

We fill up,
and we move forward.

We are that boxer
getting taken apart in the ring by a better boxer,
but we can hear our heartbeat in our head,
and it sounds like a key being punched
on a keyboard over and over again.

"fight fight
stick move
bob weave
left right
get up get up
fight fight."

It's funny how much further we'll go
if we have a reason —
or if we're inspired.

Each bell that signaled
the end of class,
also signaled the start
of the next round
in a boxing ring shaped
like a school hallway.
And my heart pounded steady:

"get up get up."

Tripped to the floor in gym class.

"get up get up."

Pushed down the stairs.

"get up get up."

Face pushed into my locker.

"get up
get your hands up
fight
defend yourself
do something
don't cry
it doesn't hurt that much.

don't cry
it's blood in the water
don't cry

get up."

15.

The first black eye
that I ever gave to someone
was an accident.

I had been given so many —
almost as if they were Valentine's Day cards,
and I was the handsome boy in class.

My grandparents saw each one,
and, late at night,
I could hear them fighting over what to do about it.

They never came up with an answer,
and it hurt me further
on the mornings when they wouldn't speak to each other.

So it surprised me when my grandmother said,

"Hit him back next time."

I had no intention of hitting anyone back —
with or without her blessing.
I was almost fourteen at that point,
and knew full well the meaning of the term "Death Wish."
It was fairly obvious that I didn't have one.
In fact,
I had something called a "Life Wish,"
a "Please Let Me Survive This Wish,"
a "If I Can Get Up and Walk Away From
   This That Would Be Great!! Wish."

Jeff had been punching me
on the shoulder all day.

I was putting on my jacket
when he did it again.
My intention was to swing around,
look him in the eye,

and say,

"Stop."

But I only had one sleeve on,
and the other arm was halfway
in my other sleeve.
When I swung around,
my elbow
caught him in the eye.

He stumbled back a few steps,
put a hand on his injured eye,
and, with the other eye,
gave me a look whose intention
could only be described as,
"if there were a cliff or tall building nearby
you would desperately be trying to unlock
the secrets of flight."

Or,

"only my dad's allowed to do that."

In return,
I gave him a look
that could only be described as,
"oh, fuck."

He gave me three hard shots to the same shoulder
he'd been punching all day,
then drove his knee into my groin,
as if he'd paid attention to a documentary about sexual
    education
and was convinced he could put an end to my lineage.

He left me there,
slumped over and gripping the floor,
like someone had taken the world by one end
and was shaking it to see if I would hang on —
or just slide over the edge and fall off,
like a crew member caught in
a Christopher Columbus nightmare.

It didn't feel like I had hit him hard,
but the next day he walked into class,
and his right eye was a smear of grey and purple.

It was like "Grimace,"
that big purple thing from McDonald's commercials,
had been shrunken to the size of a horsefly,
then trespassed into range of his windshield face.

The class whispered like a group of Secret Service men
left standing outside the bedroom door
of a diplomat visiting with a strange man.
In all probability one *"of no fixed occupation, who was
indiscriminate when it came to mingling,
and used his talents in a shameful manner
   (and usually for money).
Also "he" was (for some reason)
a bad harpsichord player,
and capable of interchanging thoughts."*

Even if one had the misfortune of being deaf,
they would still be able to sense
what the others were talking about.
You could just tell
by the way people leaned into one another —
almost kissing the ear of the listener —
as if rumor or myth was a kind of foreplay,
and everyone had just graduated from flirting.

He threw his knapsack onto his desk,
and slouched into his chair
like a bag of dog turds
being thrown onto a pile
of more bags of dog turds.

To say that he was "upset"
would be like saying the nation of Japan
was "annoyed" with Godzilla breathing radioactive fire
onto its residents and buildings.

It would be understating the facts.

I sat in my chair,
unable to think in any direction
other than the horrible retribution
that stood in front of me like an angry mountain.

If misery could imitate the luster of gold,
I would have been a prospector —
pickax in hand,
marveling at the veins,
ready to slit the wrist of this mountain,
and stake my claim in this disaster.

But retribution was like the promise of tomorrow:
it never came.
The minute hand would shake hands with the hour hand at
   midnight,
like they'd made a sinister deal
and tomorrow would go right back
to being today.

It made me think of Annie,
that red-headed orphan,
her eyes shining with optimism
as her tiny lungs blasted out that anthem of hope,
canonizing the idea of tomorrow as a better place
that could finally be reached,
and that we would make it there soon
because it's only a day away.

Sure it is.

But I suppose yesterday is, too.

16.

It was two months
after my fourteenth birthday.
I had only started defending myself,
but was astonished at the results,
and surprised at my own strength.

I was still getting my ass kicked,
but with less frequency.

It seemed that people were less likely to stage an attack
if I was more inclined to retaliate.

My life had become a kind of cold war;
both sides armed with nukes,
but neither wanting to get bombed
and suffer the fallout.

I had spent years acting out the part of a boxing bag,
and, somewhere along the way, I'd gotten so good at it
that I could take a hit and remain stoic.

I still got hurt,
but like a stripper with a special talent,
I showed it less and less,
and demanded more money for the display.

Or in my case,
more pain.

Of course, there were always those
who were willing to oblige me.

One of the worst times
involved a boy named Darren, who —
when he lost his temper — would
act like a wrestler in freak-out mode.

Unfortunately for him,
the effort
only made his face
look like a fish out of water.
And I'm sure none of what happened
would have happened,
if the movie *Stand By Me*
had never been made,
and the endearing term "Lard Ass"
was never made popular.

But it was,
and I had graduated from "FATASS"
to "Lard Ass."

"Lard" being much worse than "**FAT**"
because of both its added hilarity and hurtfulness.

(And here,
a small aside,
to the person who said "Names Will Never Hurt You."

FUCK YOU FOREVER!!!)

In any event,
Darren called me "Lard Ass."
Without thinking,
I turned around and said,

"Shut your small-fish mouth tuna face!"

Tuna.

Face.

I couldn't believe I had actually said it.

What happened to the standard "dickhead"?

You see,
every kid
has a secret arsenal of hurtful names,
and we all possess the standard weapons.
Most of them involving a colorful word
then adding the "head" to it.
But, for some reason,
while fishing around in my arsenal,
I had decided to venture past the standards
and pull out "Tuna Face."

In terms of weaponry,
it was not so much a large rusted blade,
or spiked club.
Instead,
I had pulled out a button,
and had made the very tragic mistake of pushing it.

Darren was now in full freak-out mode:
his eyes wide,
and his small mouth moving in and out,
like a tuna
out of water
desperately trying to pass oxygen through its gills.

He straddled his snowmobile.
and revved the engine.

Snow kicked up off the ground
as if it was trying to get back to the clouds,
and take the thrill ride down to earth all over again.

Maybe it was the cold that froze me in place?
Or maybe
I was just so stunned by the fact
that I had actually just affected someone
with an insult so ridiculous
as to liken someone's face
to tuna.

Whatever the reason,
I just stood there
as he raced toward me —
like I was a finish line
in some awful race,
where he was in the lead
and only meters away from the win.

The skis on his death machine bucked up
and jabbed my right side,
effectively cracking four of my ribs.
I screamed at the surprise of it.
Then,
I screamed at the pain.

Darren must have surprised himself as well,
as his face went still;
pausing to survey the damage.

He tore off into the distance,
full throttle,
almost as if he could outrun his guilt.
He carved through the snow
like a hunting knife
in the hands of a drunk.

Above me,
the northern lights continued
to dance;
my life was no concern
of theirs.

Each intake of breath was a siege,
each exhalation a revolution,
each bubbled up tear was the head of anger,
and my guillotine eyelids
ensured each one would roll.

17.

There was no lie
I could invent
to quell my grandmother's curiosity.

So,
for once,
I told her the truth.
I only left out who it was
that did it to me.

I told her I didn't know.

At school, Darren had become sheepish.
I think he scared himself when he saw what he'd done.
My injuries had achieved minor celebrity status
when they were revealed one day at gym class
after I was asked to take off my shirt.

That's the way we played basketball:
one team with shirts,
one team without.
And my dickhead of a gym teacher
insisted that I always play for the shirtless team,
even though he knew full well
about the burns and scarring on my back.

Everyone held a hand to their mouths,
shocked at the large purple-and-black nebula
floating out from under the bandages on my right side.
Even the teacher asked that I put my shirt
back on.

I had even brought that teacher a note from home
explaining that I should sit out of gym class for a while.
It was signed by my grandmother,
but he thought I was just too embarrassed,
and that wasn't a good enough reason
not to participate.

After class,
he apologized to me,
which, even after seventeen years,
continues to mean exactly jack shit to me.
Especially coming from that asshole.
For a while,
the wound acted like a black hole,
sucking in jabs from people like Jeff,
who loved seeing me wince.

But my ribs healed eventually.
And while I was on the mend,
unable to go outside
because of my grandmother's overprotective nature,
I sat at home,
watching TV,
and stumbled on to something
everyone was talking about.

Everybody in my school had become an addict
of a Canadian teen melodrama,
Degrassi Junior High.

I was no different.

I tuned in every Sunday evening,
trying to kick the static out of our old television set
to get a better reception.

The show didn't have a high production value.
The actors would not go on to win Oscars.
The show was too real for any of that —
not everyone was beautiful.

It wasn't built around stars,
or product placement.
It was built around issues
ranging from AIDS and abortion,
to molestation and relationship violence.

It was my Great Escape.
I would sit on the couch
thinking to myself,
Well, at least I'm not a fifteen-year-old pregnant girl.
Whatever else happens at least I won't have that
    to worry about.

It made my life seem less grim.

These kids weren't the kids at my school;
they were relatable.
And, though I hardly realized it at the time,
they had —
in a small way —
become my friends.
I could never call them up,
and ask to go hang out.
But it felt good to know I wasn't the only one dealing with
the great trial of growing up.

I suppose that's why everyone at my school
watched the show as well.

Their lives weren't free of regret,
or fear,
or any of the other things
that make time pass like a kidney stone.

For me,
everything was stuck
in some kind of horrible slow motion.

Only sleep
passed quickly.
And even then
I was blessed only occasionally by a flying dream,
but more frequently by wet dreams,
which
because I could not remember them,
I would have denied having altogether —
if not for the lingering evidence each morning.

"Perfectly natural,"
my granddad said
when I finally worked up the nerve to ask.

He toyed with me at first.

You see,
growing up attending a Catholic school
without any sexual education program in place,
made puberty somewhat vicious.

My voice became deeper.
Wirelike black hair began to grow in embarrassing places.
I didn't know what was happening,
and I was left with only one source to turn to.

So I asked.

He folded up his newspaper,
rested it on his lap,
looked me square in the eye,
and said,
"Maybe you're turning into a monster.
Ever think of that?"

My face sunk at his answer.

I hadn't considered the fact
that I might actually
be turning into a monster.

Then laughter thundered out him
as if Zeus had been trapped in his lungs,
and was looking for a way out.

To my further dismay,
a new episode of *Degrassi* aired later that week
in which
a character named Arthur
dealt with the exact same predicament.

If I had only waited a few more days,
I would have been spared my granddad's
sense of humor.

Anyways.

I was just sitting down to a new episode, and
my concentration was a credit card being maxed out,
when my grandmother turned off the TV.

I was furious.
I even yelled,
"What the hell?!"

My grandmother smiled at me.

Not the response I was expecting.
I thought for a moment,
and upon still being confused
asked,

"What?"

I doubt she could have smiled any wider.

"We're moving."

It was the only episode
of *Degrassi* I ever missed.

18.

It was a three-day drive south
to British Columbia's Okanagan Valley.

I didn't fidget
like I had done
on so many long drives in the past.

This was different.

I just sat back,
looked out the backseat window,
and watched the trees change.

They were thin at first.
Thin but dense.
Tundra trees,
all crowded together
like the poor at a breadline.

Slowly they became thicker,
as if they had all found work.
Their bellies were full,
and their bodies hard
from long days of holding up the sky.

Mountains shot up around us.
Their white snowcaps
timidly reminding us of where we were coming from.

But most everything else was green,
and when it wasn't green,
it was brown.
It was that least-admired color of nature
that I was quickly growing to adore.
Because, at the very least, it meant
we were coming out of a long snow-blindness.

Brown was lovely,
and when it wasn't brown
it was grey.
It was the beautiful grey
of the road stretching out in front of us,
as if it were time itself
and it never had any intention of ending.
I spent three long days
looking out the backseat window,
reinventing myself over and over again.
Smiling
at each new incarnation —
I could be anyone.

I could be that kid from the north

who knew how to skin a deer,
or set snares.
That kid everyone would call on
if they had somehow managed
to get lost in the woods overnight.

I could be that funny kid
who always knew how to make people laugh.

I could be that kid who got paid by other kids
to write locker-note-love-letters
to the girls who left boys' tongues tied,
and teachers tripping over their dropped jaws.

I could be a teacher's pet,
or a class clown,
or artistic,
or scientific.
I would probably not be athletic,
but I could be
mathematic
or historic.

I could be popular.

I could be anonymous.

I could be revered or ignored.

I could be anyone.

I could be a kid.

19.

My grandparents insisted on not needing any help
  to unpack.

Their first order of business was to get me into school,
and I didn't mind.

I was looking forward to it.

There was a quick meeting with the principal,
then an introduction to a student who would take me around
to show me the school.

She was beautiful.

The spaghetti strap

from her top

hanging just off her shoulder,

like a smile

on her arm.

Her own smile
was as warm as the inside
of our old house
on a cold day.

She took me around to my classes one at a time,
stopping to give me insider info on each teacher I would
    have.

"Okay… everybody calls this guy 'Itchy'
because he always scratches his giggle berries up and down
the corner of the desks in the front row.
Don't sit up front."

"Alright. This guy has huge arms — not muscular — just long.
Apparently, he has to get his shirts tailor-made
because his arms are so long.
  Oh and if you talk in class he'll say,
'Hello? Hello? No, no. That's rude. I'm talking now.'
It's actually kind of funny. Aside from that,
he's a really good teacher."

"There's not much to tell you about this lady,
but last year her son was ultra-drunk at the beach,
and shit his pants.
So she took him out into the lake
and washed his ass in front of everyone.
No one really bugs him about it though.
He's a super nice guy, but
his mom is just a bit strict.
Boring class,
but do the work and you'll be fine."

She asked me about the north
but all I could tell her was,
"It's cold."

She was being so nice to me,
but somehow,
each time she asked me a question,
I could only manage
to get out two-or three-word answers.

I kept cursing myself,
Come on damn you —
find common ground.
Is she menstruating?
What the hell?
You *don't menstruate.*
My grandmother stopped menstruating a year ago.
Wait.
No.
Shit.
Why do I even know that?

Words kept hitting the walls of my teeth,
and I choked them back down
like I had thrown up in my mouth
but had to swallow it
because I was standing in front of a nun.

The tour ended at my new locker.
She started to explain,

"The locks are tricky because they're so old but —"

"Actually I don't use lockers so it's okay."

"So you're just gonna carry your bag around all year?
What about your jacket and gym clothes?"

"I've just gotten used to not having a locker."

She looked at me suspiciously.

"Okay then. Have a great first day,
and don't be a stranger in the hallway."

She sauntered off.
I was left standing
at my never-to-be-used locker.

My first class would be with "Itchy."
It was unlikely that I'd get anything other than a front row
    desk
if I chose to enter class halfway through.

It was far more likely
that I would go through the awkward stage of being
    introduced
and surveyed by the class.

Their judgments slowly coming to a boil
as if their skulls were cauldrons
and they were brewing their first impressions.

And even though I had never heard of "giggle berries,"
I was somehow sure
that they were not a delicious new fruit.

In fact,
I was certain they were something more ominous,
and that I would not delight in seeing them being scratched
up and down the corner of my desk.

I decided to skip my first class.

20.

I'd gotten the hang of school pretty quickly.

I was three days into my new life —
no friends yet —
but no beatings either.

I had only just been born
as a new entity at the school.

Students slowly began to acknowledge me.
I wasn't a friend.
But I was, at the very least,
being considered.

It wouldn't be long before someone
(or some group)
extended the olive branch,
and made the effort of getting to know me.

I could feel it.
I didn't even care who did it.
In all likelihood,
I would make my best attempt to befriend
the *first* person who asked.

It happened one day
before the start of science class.

I was sitting at my table
at the back of the room.
I could see him out of the corner of my eye.
He broke away from his friends,
and walked toward me.
He stopped at the lab table.
I looked up with a smile.

He reached into his bag,
pulled out a stick of celery,
slammed it down onto the black Arborite
and said,

"It's called dieting, Fatsack."

Everyone laughed.
Except for three.

Three kids at the back of the room
did not laugh.
And oddly enough,
in a room filled with laughter,
it was their voices I heard above the rest.

I grew up with that kind of silence.

In their own quiet way
those three kids were telling me,

"You won't be left alone here either."

I felt it,
stronger than before.
One kick through the brick-wall cocoon

that I thought would keep it locked away.

It was as if a vacuum
was suddenly injected with air.
Something blazed out of me like a backdraft
licking the new meal of a firefighter
who got caught in the way.

My reaction must have looked chemical —
like one of those makeshift volcanoes at a junior-high
    science fair;
it was baking soda,
vinegar,
and red dye.

Only it wasn't dye.

His nose popped like a zit.

I could feel the sinew around his bones strain,
like a yoga master finally conceding
that there are some ways
our bodies are not meant to bend.
I felt his arm on the verge of cracking,
like a man with diminished capacity
being grilled into a confession
for a murder he had nothing to do with.

I felt another arm
slide around my throat
and squeeze tight,
like a stepfather's handshake
trying to establish dominance.

I fell back.
Full weight.
The grip loosened
and I swung around.

My fingers were sticks of dynamite with
grenades for knuckles.
My chest was a brick of C4.
My knees and elbows were blasting caps —
all of it wired into an alarm-clock head,
whose gears,
wheels,
and cogs
finally clicked past all thoughts
of past
and future,
and settled on the concept of now.

His ribs were guard rails
and I did my best to drive through them.
The last traces of peace that resided in me
pressed the accelerator,
as if the broken mess
that would be left behind
was a violence that could be loosely translated
into a suicide note.

Or,
at the very least,
a clumsy etching into a picnic table:

"Peace was here."

Peace.

WAS.

Here.

Wherever it was now,
it left no forwarding address,
and the awful thing that had moved in
took residence without leaving a damage deposit.

My lungs burned
as if newly forged,
then suddenly plunged into the water of my body,
to be hardened by a super-cooling technique
that, at the same time,
set my blood to boil.

I was mechanical now,
with an autopilot that had grown restless
after a decade-and-a-half of being set to defense.

The once-solitary fortress of my mind
had built for itself tank treads

and it slowly rolled forward to attack.

But I was no horror
that had been shaped or tempered by
the miraculous blunders that occur
when ego proposes a one-night stand to science.

I was not the misshapen offspring
that is born
when man tries to fuck nature.

I was always there.

Just underneath the surface of a skin
they forced me to shed,
so they could see what was inside.

The satisfaction of their curiosity
was my birth.

The ache of my conception —
the agony of my being carried to term —
would now be counted against them
with an interest rate that made sure
their labor pains would make me rich.

It was a pregnancy in reverse;
now that I had been delivered
their discomfort would begin.

It felt good
to finally introduce myself.
I dipped my head low,
taking a bow,
and now, being so far beyond reason,
I thought,

Perfectly natural.
After all, I could have been anyone.

21.

The principal's office at my new school
was different.

No cheap, plastic crucifix
hanging on the wall.

No poorly framed pictures of jesus
with light pouring off him
like god's first attempt at building a flashlight.

There were only hokey, motivational posters:

"Your mind is a parachute — it only works when it's open."

And one with a superimposed infant
on the edge of a cliff.
   The caption read:
"Hang in there baby!!!"

My new principal
was a breed of idiot
that I had never encountered.

He fumbled.

Trying to connect to a generation of students
now so alien to him.
It was as if his school was a landing pad or,
a way station where people stopped only briefly,
then continued on their way through some great cosmos,
which he had only ever heard about.

He was always being left behind.

I wondered if those posters were there for him.

It was impossible to tell.

He was different.

He didn't try to intimidate me with long silences
or heavy sighs.
His voice was calm — gentle even.
His questions were not commands.

"Would you like to talk about what happened?"

I almost laughed,
assuming that this was some new method
of garnering my confession.

If it was,
it was pathetic.

"No."

He pulled out a file and opened it.

"I'm just puzzled.
The transcript from your last school shows you to be
a bright and attentive student.
Good grades.
An aptitude for history."

He closed the file.

"I see this from time to time with new students,
they have trouble leaving their old friends behind and — "

Without meaning to,
I laughed out loud.

What friends?

I was amazed the file said nothing about
the beatings,
or the bullying,
the constant mocking,
and the name calling.

Did my old school just leave that stuff out?
If they pretended it never happened
maybe,
one day,
I'd believe the same thing?

I was done crying about it.

All I could do was laugh.

My grandmother entered the room,
holding her purse in front of her like
it was an old, Styrofoam coffee cup,
and she had come begging for something.

The principal sat up a little straighter,

"I called your grandmother down here
so we could sort this all out."

Disappointment was scrawled across her face
like the crayon-scribble drawings
of a child whose imagination
had been amputated by doctors —
just to see what would happen.

My heart was a message in a bottle
being sent down a stream,
now rapidly approaching a waterfall.

I could feel her frustration stabbing at me.
Slowly the stabbing became sawing.
Her eyes rested on me like the world's last sunset,
and I felt the steady unease of a shadow
sweeping the remaining light into a dust pan.

In my quest to be
what I became,
I had become a regret to her.

In addition to that,
my principal filled in the blank
that hadn't even occurred to me:

"Your grandson is a bully."

Your grandson is a bully...

Part 7

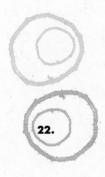

22.

I could stand in the middle of the hallway
during lunch hour,
and waves of students would just rush around me
as if I were a boulder in a river.

My reputation spread as if I had chicken pox,
and every other student was locked in a room with me
so they would get it, too.

Rumors grew like crops,

and everyone around me

harvested them like truths.

I was happy to let them.

I mixed their opinions of me
with more fighting,
and quickly cemented their estimations into hard facts.

I pushed my hands firmly into the wet concrete
  of their lives
and watched it dry;
watched it harden like acceptance
finally settling in,
after witnessing something unbelievable.

The last period
in the previous chapter of my life
was a bullet hole,
fired deep into the chest
of whatever it was
I used to be.

I could hear the hard swallow of their acceptance
each time I passed by.

Their eyes stuck to the floor
as if a magnet was pulling their gaze
away from me.

And if, by chance,
they met my stare,
they would suddenly melt like wax,
and later harden into a candle
that their family would light
in prayer of a safe passage to heaven.

But each time they would melt,
they would be remade into another candle.
They would burn over and over again,
until they eventually threw up their hands to god
and begged to be forgotten.

I never went out of my way
to torment someone.

They were not particularly dry leaves
on a sidewalk
that would break my stride —
just so I could step on them
and hear the satisfying crunch.

But I would,
from time to time,
act without reason.

My arms would unfurl like two flails,
then thrash through someone,
as if their bones were a birthday present
covered by the wrapping paper of their flesh.

No one did anything to me.

But like some heathen god,
my reputation would demand sacrifice
to ensure its survival.
And what made me more terrible
than any of the others who would accept offerings
in exchange for appeasement,
was that I had no criteria for my victims.

I did not actively target anyone
according to any specifications.

I was a chef
at a twenty-four hour diner.

I was always open.

And I served
everyone.

23.

School was adjusting to me.
It was a nice little role reversal that I was starting to enjoy.
But my life at home had transmuted into something
   unfamiliar.

My moods would shift
like tectonic plates,
and each time anger tremored out of me,
I could hear my grandparents
rattling together like two ceramic bowls
placed on top of one another.

It was as if we were tethered
only by the flimsy excuse of genetics.

A thin cord
that could snap at any time,
and hurl me out into the world
with all the momentum of a stone
trained against believing in the propaganda of gravity
and wind resistance.

I began cutting myself
with a scalpel

that I had stolen from the science lab.

Small,
at first.
But as time passed,
I became more confident.

I had a drawer in my desk
dedicated to the safe keeping
of bandages,
gauze,
hydrogen peroxide,
small blades,
razors,
needles,
pins,
anything sharp.

I was intrigued at how different instruments
would leave different scars.

A razor, for example,
was perfect for straight lines
that left the scar tissue looking like a bubbled-up
white line.
It looked like a small worm
that you could just peel off your body.

A sharp piece of glass, on the other hand,
was never quite as delicate.
It didn't so much cut,
as it did rip open.
The evidence of its use
looked like a dirt-path shortcut
that had been erased from a roadmap
because its existence could never be confirmed.

Over time,
I began to develop different techniques,
which yielded different results.

I used to take a piece of thread,
wind it tightly around my index finger,
then wait for my fingertip to look and feel
like it was about to burst.
And when I couldn't take it anymore,
I would jab the tip with a safety pin,
quickly unravel the thread,
then exhale the deep satisfaction of release.

I bought a stopwatch
and started to time my efforts.
I tried to push the limits of how long I could wait;
the greater the tease,
the greater the release.

I used to heat the tip of a needle or pin,
and slowly push it through my fingernail
until it broke through into the flesh.

It was something I'd learned from my granddad.
He crushed his finger in a door once,
and as it began to swell he performed the procedure
at the kitchen table.

I remember being impressed with the way
  he bore the pain,
and, upon knowing what it felt like,
was impressed all the more.
But of all my processes,
the one that I came to adore,
was a thin — but deep — cut to my knee.

It would take such a long time to heal,
because every time I walked or sat,
every time I bent my knee,
the cut would reopen
like a stubborn fast food restaurant
owner who was convinced he could compete
with the franchises.

Sometimes,
if it would begin to heal too quickly,
I would stretch the surrounding skin in opposite directions,
and slowly reopen the wound myself.

On one particularly daring day,
I pushed myself a little too far.
The razor moved a little too swiftly.
It cut a little too deeply.

The wound was something not easily remedied
by any of the contents in my desk drawer.

Within minutes,
the white cloth I was using to control the damage
was a red mess.

I calmly called my grandmother downstairs,
and when she finally arrived to investigate
I looked up from what I had done,
and met her horrified gaze.

"I can't make it stop."

We sat in the back seat of my grandfather's car.
He drove quickly but safely.

She had grabbed a large towel from the bathroom,
and I could feel it soaking through.
But every time I would try to look at what was happening
she would put her hand on my face
and turn me back to her.
She would use two fingers and point to her eyes,

"Eyes here."

We arrived at the hospital without incident,
and the surgeon in emergency
managed to patch me up.

Then came the questions.

They sent in a shrink
armed with a clipboard,
and a ballpoint pen.

What happened?

What are all these other scars from?

How long have you been cutting yourself?

Etc.

I kept my answers as brief as possible.

The shrink disappeared behind the curtain,
and I could hear his conversation with my grandmother,
suggesting that I see another shrink.

Not long after that, she poked her head
    through the curtain.

"Can I come in?"

"Yeah."

She pulled up a stool next to me,
I could feel the sterile, tissue sheet underneath
    me crinkling
as I tried to brace myself
for what I thought was about to come.
They had mentioned boarding school to me before,
and I had always shrugged it off,
as if it would make no difference to me
one way or the other.

Of course it would.

I would have to start all over again
in some strange place,
locked down by the heavy fist of discipline.

I feared the worst,
big brother,
thought police,
public showers.

Public showers.
To most people that would be a joke.
To most people it wouldn't be a big deal.
Most people
could shower publicly,
and not be stared at,
or laughed at.
Not feel clouds of disgust rising like steam
from the hot water.

Most people would feel clean after a shower.

I only ever felt ashamed and more hideous.

I remembered
wet towels snapping at my ass.
I remembered
being surrounded by a makeshift convention
of lion tamers in training.

It was a game to them.

I was thrown out of my memory,
and back into the emergency room,
when my grandmother asked,

"Why are you doing this?"

"Because."

My mind raced back to Chris
and the day I asked him why he was bullying me.
His answer was the same as mine:

"Because."

Did I even have a reason?

I had come so far from that place
where I could be beaten
or hurt.

Why was I doing this to myself?

Was pain a long-lost friend
whom I had grown to miss?

I was given pause to think about what I was doing.

"Because" wasn't a reason.
It was a gigantic stone
sitting heavily at the entrance of a cave,
and I would have to find some way
to push it aside,
then search for the reason behind it.

It seemed immovable.

My Inner Construction Crew had long since vanished.
My Inner Community had left my body behind,
turning it into some sort of ghost town.
A place where only wind would dare to venture,
and lightly blow dust through the leftover buildings and
    playgrounds,
as if time were a shovel that could eventually bury all of it.

I had only that *thing* to call on,
that *thing* who had probably placed that boulder there
in the first place.

It stood beside me,
stoic as a pyramid
left standing after the entire world's population
had died off.

My small request
for the removal of the boulder
bounced off it
like a small pebble
hitting a brick wall.

I repeated myself
over and over again
until it finally began to move.

Its fist cocking back
like the hammer of a gun
preparing to fire its concentrated strength
at the boulder that blocked my way.

Contact
was like opening the door
of a warm peaceful home
and stepping out into a tornado.

Dust spun around me like a cocoon,
wrapping me in doubt.
My mind was in metamorphosis
my resolve slowly transforming
into second thoughts.

But it was too late,
the boulder was a pile of small rocks.
Large clouds of loose sand
slowly descended to the ground,
like an alien-invasion force
landing on Earth for the first time.

My whole world
was a puzzle that had been
momentarily tossed into the air.
And I was amazed
to watch all the pieces fall
and settle back into place.

I watched myself climb out of the mouth of the cave,
a small remote control in one hand,
and a razor in the other.
I looked at me and spoke,

"He doesn't take batteries.
He doesn't work like that.

Watch."

I saw myself cutting into my arm;
a small river of blood snaked toward to my hand
where I held the remote.
It was like a magnet pulling my blood into it.

There was a rumble as the blood made contact,
and the small black box lit up for a moment.

The *thing* beside me
knelt down in a Thinking-Man pose.

Was this my reason?

Was I hurting myself
to keep myself angry?

Was I torturing myself
to keep this *thing* alive?

I looked over to my grandmother still sitting beside me,

"Because...
Because I'm tired of being scared."

Because I'm tired of being scared...

Part 8

24.

I'll never know if boarding school was an empty threat.

My grandmother and I were talking again.
I could feel her relief
as I let her back inside.

It washed over me, as well.
It was good to have someone to talk to.
I didn't relish the idea of going to a shrink,
so I doubled my efforts
in talking with her.

I made sure she knew how I was feeling.
Made sure she knew what was going on in my life.

We emptied out my desk drawer together.
Threw out all of my tools.

It looked so hollow;
like a small home
whose inhabitants
had packed up and moved out.

Over time,
it became my junk drawer.

A drawer dedicated to the purpose of housing
all of the little things
that I somehow
could not bring myself to throw away.

Old pennies.
Useless pens.
Staples.
Glue sticks.
Tape.

Things that I never really needed
but kept —
just in case.

I stopped cutting altogether,
and turned my attention to an old science set.

I began growing peas.

My grandmother suggested it,
said that it might help me learn patience and,
at the same time,
fill my need for anticipation.

It was frustrating to learn
that she was always right.

I kept a notebook
to mark progress,
and measure growth.

I wrote down the recipes
for growth formulas,
and charted which ones
yielded the best results.

I learned the germination process.

I grew a small forest of plants,
and labeled each
with the names of my past tormentors.

I felt powerful —
in a very small way —
knowing, that at any
given time,
I could just grab the lot
of them,
and toss them into
the garbage.

But each day I returned from school,
and headed to my room
to check on their progress.

There was a tremendous sense of satisfaction
in knowing I had grown them.

It was strange.

I hated peas.

But to watch them finally push through the soil
and stretch upward —
like the arms of a yawning giant
waking from a long sleep —
instilled me with pride.

"Chris"
was the only one
that I was tempted to torture;
tempted to let die of thirst.
I almost wanted that plant to suffer.

But, in a way,
I paid more attention,
showed more affection
to "Chris"
than any of the other plants.

It was silly.
I mean they were plants.

They weren't there to judge me
based on what kind of clothes I wore,
or what I looked like.

They just stood there,
stiff and self-conscious
like a group of eighth-grade boys
lined up against the gym wall
at a school dance.

I could hardly believe it at the time,

but those small plants
who counted on me
for light
and water
were not just some hobby.

They were my friends.

25.

Trying to make "real" friends at school
was like getting an erection
in the middle of math class
for no reason.

It was hard.

My reputation was a nuclear reactor
that had gone through meltdown.

The fallout was everywhere,
and the winds of change
swept through the school
pushing it out into the rest of the world.

There was far too much damage
for any of it to be contained.

Students had become mutations,
and whenever I was present
their confidence would fall
around them like clumps of hair.

Their mouths would seal themselves shut,
and I could hear their moans and whimpers
trapped like echoes in the deep caverns of their throats.

Their hearts
had become a kind of third kidney,
pumping foulness through the sewer system
of their veins.

They hated me.

And why shouldn't they?

Just as I hated those who tortured me
with their threats of violence.
They had every right
to feel the same.

I was surprised that there was no
drumhead court martial
to string me up;
kick the barrel out from under me,
and hang me for what I'd done.

There was no summary judgment
made against me.
No swift punishment
to balance out the scales of justice

and lend relief to those
I had victimized.

Shame pressed its lips to mine,
as if I were a captive
in a shotgun wedding.

Behind me was Regret,
with its finger on the trigger,
ready to do me in
if I did not concede
and do the honorable thing.
As if there was ever any honor
to be found in anything done
without love at the core of its reason.

I failed to see what happened.
And change drifted in like a caravan of settlers
staking claim to land
that was already occupied.

It was simple enough to see now.

My reputation owned me.

Any act of genuine kindness
was met with suspicion and fear.

One day a kid dropped a book in the hallway.
I bent down to pick it up.
I extended my arm,
offering it back to him.

He looked at it for a moment,

like a diamond monger
trying to appraise its worth.

He looked at me,
trying to weigh
whether the book
was worth whatever price
I might charge him
for taking it back.

As if the price I had in mind
was a pound of flesh,
or an ounce of tears.

The kid turned around and walked away,
leaving me holding his textbook.

I was insulted.
I could feel the kick at my gut.

I could feel "him"
dragging his finger back and forth
along prison bars, like a steel cup.
"He" was trying to get my attention.

I could feel "him"
trying to bribe his way out,
offering me satisfaction
in exchange for freedom.

Temptation whispered into my ear seductively.
Its wet suggestion
lingering like a sunrise on pause.

My immediate instinct
was to throw the book
at the back of the kid's head.

I followed him instead.

He didn't look back once,
and weaved swiftly
through the current of students.

I had the benefit of a reputation;
it walked out in front of me
clearing my path
like some kind of invisible bulldozer
splitting the crowd like a curtain.

There was a time, not long ago,
I would have imagined their bloodied faces
dripping roses onto the empty space
of my intended footsteps.

Now there was only the hallway.

I watched the kid rush into his classroom
like a rabbit down a hole,
believing in the false safety of hiding.

I entered behind him

like some terrible monster,

ripping up the earth

all around him.

Exposing him

like a meal

being unwrapped

by hungry hands.

He looked up at me from his desk,
and from behind his eyes
I could recognize
his thoughts.

They raced from one awful expectation
to the next.
Accelerating at each thought,
as if the finish line was a myth —
but better to trust a hope
than to live like this forever.

Temptation tried again.
Its thin fingers
sliding in under my skin
and grabbing some hidden part inside my body
that made me feel amazing.

Shame squeezed my hand.
A gentle reminder that the alchemy of time
can easily transform satisfaction
into regret.

I placed the book on his desk.

"You dropped this."

26.

It wasn't that simple.

One good deed
couldn't erase everything I'd done.

There was no quick-fix remedy
that could throw everything into reverse.

I didn't have the resources
or the knowledge
to build a time machine.

I couldn't go back and warn myself
what would come of the choices I made.
Couldn't throw myself up against a locker
and lay out the entire story
like a scary tale at a campfire.

Armed, finally, with the wisdom of hindsight,
and hard lessons learned,
there was no way to rewind.
I could offer no parable to my former self.

And even if I could,
would I bother listening to myself?
Or would I remain consumed
by my need to feed *"him?"*

There was no wacky
time-traveling adventure
in my future.

I remember the teacher with huge arms
lecturing my class
on how history is written by the winners,
and that's why the winners
are always the good guys.

I wondered:
if the Nazis had won the war,
if they would be heroes instead of
the axis of evil?

Would there be anyone left
to dispute their reputation as the good guys?

It sounded preposterous
in the same way the truth sometimes does.
But if they did somehow manage to write the history books
would I question their politics?

Or would I have enough strength of spirit
to deny their actions?

Could I, through study,
arrive at the conclusion
that all history is the toxic byproduct
of propaganda?

Is there a reason that
truth becomes fiction
when you finally write it down?

And who was I?

A hero or a victim?

Or did I just sit on the fence
weighing the options forever —
too scared to stake a claim in either destiny?

I could not liken myself
to people of note
throughout history.

It was simple.

I was a scratch-and-win lotto ticket.
No.
I wasn't even that.
I was the small bonus scratch-and-win
at the bottom-right-hand corner of the ticket.
Anyone who took the time
to scratch the thin surface away
would discover something
that they probably knew all along.

I was "Not a Winner."

I can only tell you how it felt...

Part 9

27.

I kept to myself mostly.

There was no great

turn around

that made my life any better.

No sudden flood of popularity

to wash away my reputation.

People left me alone;

all of them fearful of a reawakening.
As if the thing inside me
had found slumber,
and everyone around
was blessed by a shortage of sticks
with which to poke him —
and an acute wisdom telling them not to.

It was a relief
to finally see them heed the advice
of their Inner Communities.
As if experience was a village elder
gravely warning them,
"You leave that thing alone."

They had learned
that some limits
are better left unchallenged.
That some monsters
are real.

And while they may not drool blood,
or wield jagged claws
made from the broken ribs
of their victims,
they are hungry.
And they have no eyes to determine
what it is they're eating,
and no disposition to care.

Afterword.

I was never meant to be this thing.

But it's how I learned to survive.
It was my reason.
It was my "because."

And the "why"
is so much simpler.

The "why"
is just a question
that would never have been asked
if I didn't choose to live.

In our own way,
we were all like Pinocchio
searching for some way
to finally be made real.

But we lied too much
and our noses grew,
stretching our sense of smell
out of proportion.

We were left to blindly sniff out
some semblance of who we truly were.

We were scared.

We'd huddle together in classrooms,
like children around a campfire
being told the horror story of the world.
And then we were told
it would all be our responsibility.
Soon.

We were terrified.

It was a fear bigger than any monster
Hollywood could dream of.

So we wore thin shells of false bravery,
and marched out into the world
with our lives set to defense —
never knowing how completely we shielded ourselves
from understanding
one another.

We were frightened.

Fear gripped us
like a lover who refuses to let go,
because it knows
that in loneliness
it cannot exist.

The story of our lives unfolds only once,
and each time a page is turned,
we force ourselves into knowing
that we can never edit or rewrite
our past.

We move closer and closer to an ending.
And we can only hope
that when we read ourselves,
the story will unfold lucidly enough
to teach us something.

You see,
we never made it to that place
I called Away.
My mother never came back for me.
And the bag I kept packed
for the day I hoped she would,
is now only a memory.

She was there for my graduation,
and she saw the same thing I did —
graduation was the end
of a conveyor belt
built to produce a new generation
of prototype adults.

Adults who were never taught
that even in the face of our differences and beliefs,
symmetry can be achieved.

That beauty is a choice
when it is embraced —
those who deny it
are only admitting their blindness.

Not long after graduation,
my mother died —
and I hated her for it.

I hated her
as if death was a choice she made,
and she didn't care
that she was leaving me behind.

I watched her die,
slowly,
as if she was giving me the time to ask her something
that I didn't know how to ask.

So she spoke instead,
and she told me,

"Time moves like a blade against the grain of our wrists.
It tells us that we will one day leave this place.

So pack lightly.

Do not weigh yourself down with heavy bags of regret."

She didn't mean to die,
it just happened.

Her story ended,
and became a chapter in my own.

And every question
that I kept loaded with hate —
questions like,
"Where were you?"
and
"How could you?"
fell through my fingers,
fell through the cracks in the sidewalk,
and fell
and fell
and fell.

When I went to her tiny apartment
and saw how the disease took her
one piece at a time,
like a game of chess
against an invisible opponent
that she never had any hope of beating.

I stood at her closet and felt
a new question punch me in the gut:

*"Now that you're gone,
what should I do with your clothes?"*

I felt that thing inside me roar
with a voice like an air-raid siren.
But it wasn't angry this time,
just wounded.

As if somewhere deep inside of its mechanics —
past its mindlessness,
beyond its wires and engineering —
there was something small,
where the gears held no territory,
where it could feel.

My grandmother once said,
"Every person is made up of a community.

They live inside of you.
If you feed them,
clothe them,
care for them,
they'll grow up to be strong.

And they'll lend you their strength
when you call for it.

If you don't ignore them,
you can lead them."

I wish you could understand it
as fundamentally as only experience can explain.

I wish you could know it
as intimately as only romance can allow,
or as intricately as only skin can translate.

But, it's like I said.

I can only tell you how it felt.

I can only tell you
that every time I forgave them,
my entire world twisted in anguish.

I can only tell you
that every time I say "I'm sorry,"
that thing inside me
sounds out like a banshee,
promising to shake me apart from the inside out.

But, like loving someone
who was never there for you,

I do it anyways.

About the author...

You only have to hear spoken-word virtuoso **Shane. L. Koyczan** once to be hooked — humane, furious, sexy, political, tragic, and so funny you'll be laughing through your tears. Koyczan's performances — thrillingly rich, fast, and cool — have brought audiences to their feet in New York, London, Edinburgh, Sydney, Auckland, and Los Angeles.

Winner of the US Slam Poetry Championship and Canadian Spoken Word Olympics, Shane has been featured on BRAVO television, and NPR, BBC, CBC, and ABC (Australia) radio. His first published collection, *Visiting Hours,* was the only work of poetry selected by both the *Guardian* and the *Globe and Mail* for their Best Books of the Year lists.

Stickboy is Shane's very first novel... but certainly not his last.

Praise for *Visiting Hours* and Shane. L. Koyczan...

Best Books of the Year Selection 2005, *The Guardian*
Best Books of the Year Selection 2005, *The Globe and Mail*

Val McDermid, author:
"Shane Koyczan is electrifying."

Colum McCann, IMPAC nominee:
"There'll be comparisons aplenty — Gary Snyder, Leonard Cohen,
Nick Cave — but Koyczan is staking out his own literary acreage
for himself. Koyczan employs a mysterious light touch to rip open
your ribcage. Allow it."

Patrick Neate, winner of the Whitbread Prize:
"Shane is a real star."

The Guardian:
"[Koyczan] makes you feel the depth of love, joy, and pain
in everyday life."

New Zealand Herald:
"...[I]f the [Auckland Writers and Readers] festival had a Supreme
Award, Canadian performance poet Shane Koyczan would have won
it, packing out the lower theatre and receiving a standing ovation."

Sydney Morning Herald:
"Shane Koyczan was a hit. His raw poems about love, sex and
cancer made the audience laugh and cry. Along with [Ayaan] Hirsi
Ali, he received one of the festival's passionate standing ovations."

Write OutLoud London:

"Shane has a way with words and a delivery that had the seasoned poets and actors present literally gasping, clapping, and slapping their thighs mid-poem. My neighbour was in tears, clutching her face for much of the set. Always accessible but by turns hilarious, deeply moving, and profound, often in the same poem, this was a truly awesome set delivered by a prodigious talent..."

The Scotsman:

(Reviewing the Edinburgh Book Festival, 2005)

"Finally then, it's time to hand out a few awards. Best chairman: Ian Rankin. Books we now must read: Sebastian Barry's *A Long, Long Way*. Best poetry reading: Shane Koyczan. Best superstar: Salman Rushdie."

About House of Parlance Media...

House of Parlance is a new media company and trade book publisher inspired by literary and visual storytelling. We work with authors, writers, artists, illustrators, and spoken word poets. From high-quality titles to electronic media, our works promote new connections between artists, authors, and their worldwide audiences.

We find emerging talent from the 21st century's richest and most-potent creative incubator: *everywhere*. We're currently working on several new titles for kids, adults, and everyone in between. We will also publish some fresh poetry and spoken-word titles from some of the finest voices out there.

Check out our website at *www.houseofparlance.com*

Additional titles from House of Parlance Media:

How I Learned to Run (2008) by Kinnie Starr
Visiting House (2005) by Shane. L. Koyczan

"I was never meant to be this thing..."

My fingers were sticks of dynamite with
grenades for knuckles.
My chest was a brick of C4.
My knees and elbows were blasting caps —
all of it wired into an alarm-clock head,
whose gears,
wheels,
and cogs
finally clicked past all thoughts of past
and future,
and settled on the concept of now. ...

But I was no horror that had been shaped or tempered by
the miraculous blunders that occur
when ego proposes a one-night stand to science.

I was not the misshapen offspring
who is born
when man tries to f— nature.

I was always there. ...

This is award-winning author and poet
Shane. L. Koyczan's powerful first novel with
House of Parlance Media.

FRONT COVER DESIGN AND ILLUSTRATION: *John Rummen*
BACK COVER AND INTERIOR DESIGN: *Mauve Pagé*

house of parlance
media inc.

www.houseofparlance.com

ISBN 978-0-9738131

9 780973 813